The Honey Shop

by Maria Kathe
illustrated by Joy Allen

Harcourt

Orlando   Boston   Dallas   Chicago   San Diego

www.harcourtschool.com

1

"I'm bored," said Queen Bee-Bee. "All I do all day is sit around in this hive."

"Me too," said Queen Buzz. "Every day is the same. What can we do?"

"Let's open a honey shop!" said Queen
 Bee-Bee.

4

"Bee-Bee, remember the last time we tried that? We forgot to hire a guard, and someone ate all our honey," said Queen Buzz. "We went out of business."

"We'll know better this time, Buzz!" said
Bee-Bee. "Let's give it a try. We can hire
someone big and strong to guard the honey
for us."

"I'll send 23 bees to the clover patch," said Bee-Bee. "And I'll send 25," said Buzz.

Bee-Bee decided to send 36 bees to the orange tree. They would be joined by 32 of Queen Buzz's bees.

Queen Bee-Bee would send 43 bees
to the wildflowers. Queen Buzz would
send 12.

Soon the hives were buzzing with bees making honey. "I think we're ready to open, Buzz," said Queen Bee-Bee. "Did you hire a guard?"

"Yes—I got the biggest, strongest one I could find. I don't think we have to worry now!"

11

12